PORCELAIN PROMPTS
CONFLICT & RESOLUTION

ISBN: 978-1-947269-01-9

TABLE OF CONTENTS

WRITING CHECKLIST:

1) PORCELAIN PROMPTS… CHECK!
2) YOUR AWESOME WRITING SKILLS… CHECK!
3) THRONE TO SIT UPON… we'll let you answer this one…
4) PORCELAIN PROMPTS PEN/PENCIL…
5) BOOKMARK…

Don't have a Number 2 ready for your next prompt? We meant pencil. You can get a Porcelain Prompts bookmark, pen or pencil for free when you come see us at one of our appearances! Check the social medias (Facebook, Twitter, Instagram, YouTube) to find out where and when or check us out at SpinePressandPost.com

NOW, LET'S GET TO WRITING!

PROMPT 1: FIGHTING WITH MYSELF

Man vs. Self: Write a scene featuring the internal conflict of your protagonist debating with themselves about a task at hand. Why are they unsure if they should/could do it? What is holding them back?

Prompt 1

PROMPT 2: NOT WORKING FOR THE MAN

Man vs. Society: Write a scene where an individual must fight against unjust laws or regulations. Why are they fighting this system? What is flawed about the society that needs to be changed? Why do the laws or regulations exist in the first place?

Prompt 2

PROMPT 3: MAN VS. MAN

Man vs. Man: Write a fight scene (verbal or physical) between two people. Why do they disagree? Why do they both think they are right? Why do they think the other person is wrong?

COMBINING CONFLICT: TOO MUCH ADDITION BECOMES SUBTRACTION

Thomas A. Fowler

"There's too many things to follow!" It happens a lot in current storytelling. Many people are so obsessed with building their larger "universe" they forget to tell a singular story that works. (Cough "Amazing Spiderman 2" cough "The Mummy" cough) Excuse me.

A great (well, great for the purpose of what not to do in this discussion) example is "Batman v. Superman: Dawn of Justice." In the comic adaptation of the story where the Caped Crusader and the Man of Steel duke it out, it was over more of an idealistic difference, not because they were put together due to a kidnapped character where they resolve their differences because they have to save Martha. Sorry, didn't give that the right delivery: "Save.....MARTHAAAA!!!!"A major issue with the movie is that they, conservatively, tried telling four separate stories in a single narrative.

First, there was the "Man of Steel" sequel where they asked "does the world need Superman?" Which, by itself, could have been a complete narrative and is a great question but it's barely broached and then *SPOILER* Superman gets axed and we get the answer but it was, arguably, a small afterthought.

The second narrative was a "Batman" standalone where he's returning to his investigative roots— which could've been a great, noir-style take on Batman.

Third, was the "Batman versus Superman" narrative which we had no established background with the characters to build from outside of an opener where Bruce was retroactively inserted.

Finally, we had the assembling of the Holy Trinity (Batman, Superman, and Wonder Woman) to face Doomsday. As a result, it was a jumbled mess.

In the comic, the writers acknowledged the long history of Batman and Superman, in which they fundamentally disagreed on the best approach to justice. Superman believed in being a bright beacon:

transparent, open, and willing to be a symbol of hope. Batman, who at this point was nearing the end of his run because of old age and nagging injuries, was bitter, having lost too much. He refused to operate cleanly and worked in shadows, being a symbol of fear. That's a great narrative and the movie hinted at this conflict but then abandoned the notion to make Lex Luthor the big bad, instead. But then, just kidding, Lex isn't the big bad.

Conflict kept getting added and added without letting a single idea flesh itself out entirely. Had all of these movies been explored separately, the moment *SPOILER AGAIN* Superman decides this is his world and sacrifices himself to stop Doomsday would've been so much more impactful. We would have received a proper amount of time getting to know the characters and dived into the concepts of "does the world need Superman?" and who is on the right side of justice versus fear? Instead, studio execs tried to catch up to the Marvel Cinematic Universe in a single movie.

An *actual* great example of conflict providing incredible tension and storytelling is "Die Hard." We take our time to get to know John McClane, and the conflict is simple: international terrorists take over a building to hijack a fortune; McClane is the out-of-town cop who can stop them. Yes, there are subplots and more details in the overall narrative, such as the complications the police and federal agents cause outside of the building and the sensitive relationship of John and his estranged family. However, everything in that story boils down to that singular conflict and everything else exists to serve that central conflict, build tension, and to make the characters relatable. That's why we were able to summarize "Die Hard" in a single sentence with an easy-to-understand conflict front and center.

Now, here's a challenge outside of a writing prompt: try to summarize "Batman v. Superman: Dawn of Justice" in a single sentence with only one central conflict. The movie just kept building and building and adding and adding. If you can do it in a sentence, you're likely skipping out on major plot points because here are all the conflicts introduced (yet none of which serve a singular purpose) that we have to deal with:

- Earth and the civilian population respond to Superman's methods used to fight Emperor Zod.
- Batman and Superman's conflict rises because Superman caused such destruction fighting Zod (separate from the above

because Bruce Wayne and Batman don't play into the trial from the populace).

- Batman investigates Lex Luthor about all of the superheroes showing up in the Gotham/Metropolis area.
- Wonder Woman helps Batman with the investigation including the notion of assembling a team to fight a looming evil outside of Lex Luthor.
- Lex Luthor is obtaining alien artifacts from Krypton to stop Superman.
- Lex Luthor is working for a higher being (Steppenwolf. Nope. Just kidding. Darkseid).
- Lex Luthor is creating Doomsday from Zod's body.
- Lex Luthor also pits Batman and Superman against one another, initially using their differences of ideals, then kidnapping Superman's mother and forcing him to take down Batman to stop the investigation Batman is taking on (with Wonder Woman's help).
- Superman, Batman, and Wonder Woman have to unite to stop the newly created Doomsday.

In summary, it's fine to add subplots and additional conflict types to your narrative. (Read the book versions of "Jurassic Park" and "Jaws" for perfect examples because much more occurs in those books that you don't see in the movies, but all additional conflicts still work themselves into the main narrative purpose.) However, it all has to work toward a single conflict that has to be resolved because, going back to the "Die Hard" reference, everything that happens with the subplots helps us with the characters and central conflict. John's marriage is seemingly on the mend because the husband and wife realize their previous issues meant nothing after surviving the conflict. In addition, Reginald V. Johnson's character, Sgt. Powell the local cop, helps deal with the incompetent federal agents and they are put on the sidelines to let McClane stop Hans Gruber. Every subplot and side character served the larger conflict.

When in doubt: keep it simple so you can focus on building tension and characters. The best examples of writing all do that.

Melissa elaborates on the issues facing "Batman v. Superman: Dawn of Justice," in her article "Let's Talk About Martha" a little later. Enjoy!

PROMPT 4: MAN VS. NATURE

Man vs. Nature: Write a scene where a person must survive in an inhospitable environment. How will they outlast the dangers? What resources do they have? Is there an opportunity to escape it?

Prompt 4

PROMPT 5: MAN VS. SUPERNATURAL

Man vs. Supernatural: Write a scene where an average person must defend against magical or alien forces. How can they fight off something that defies the physics of Earth? What creative problem solving can they accomplish?

Prompt 5

Prompt 5

PROMPT 6: COMBO

Write a scene that utilizes two types of conflict (i.e.: Man vs. Man, Man vs. Technology, etc.) How do the two conflict types work together for the character's singular quest? Why do they both have to exist?

Prompt 6

Prompt 6

FIVE WAYS TO INCREASE CONFLICT ARTICLE

Thomas A. Fowler

If you ever find yourself struggling to increase conflict, or a chapter isn't feeling tense enough, there are some very tangible ways you can up the stakes. Who are we kidding, "If" is a big misnomer. It should say "When" because you have to constantly increase conflict and make your characters struggle to achieve what they want. Otherwise, they're vanilla heroes and the conflict feels completely uninteresting. Always, always increase conflict.

Here are five ways to do so:

1. Follow the rule of "No" or "Yes, but…" Your character wants to achieve something, stop evil, find inner peace, resolve a problem with a friend or family member, etc. but in order to keep conflict, you have to make two choices until they ultimately overcome their central obstacle. First choice is "No." This is where your central character did not achieve it with their latest attempt; therefore, they have to keep going and find a new way to get what they want. The other option is "Yes, but…" This is where the character seemingly achieves the goal they sought out for, but for one reason or another something else is in their way, or getting what they wanted wasn't what they expected, and they therefore have to change their game plan to still achieve their central goal. (Watch the TV show "Silicon Valley" for great examples. Nearly every episode ends with a "No" or "Yes, but…")
2. Make your character fail. It sounds simple, but honestly, what happens if your hero just straight up fails at something? It causes rifts with other characters, increases stakes, and makes them human because when was the last time in your life you got exactly what you wanted the first time you tried? In stories, when characters succeed too much or too easily, it loses relatability and the tension disappears because the characters aren't interesting. Think about when Mark Watney's potato farm is destroyed in "The Martian." It blows up (literally, in

this case) what we expected from the final act and increases the stakes so much for everyone trying to bring Watney home!

3. Tie everything together. Read the previous article about too many conflicts. If your conflict feels disconnected it may be because you can't summarize your conflict in a single sentence. Write your story's main conflict down. If you can't do it in a single sentence, it's likely too much. So refine it. Then, once you do, any chapters lacking conflict you need to tie into that simple, central conflict. Make it all connected so it works toward building the resolution of said conflict. If you can't tie it to your central obstacle, then rewrite the chapter or remove it. The section may just be a good character exploration, or it could be unexpected correlation that gives you new revelations regarding your story and characters. ("Die Hard," which is also in the article about too much conflict.)
4. Put your characters in unfamiliar circumstances. This can either be the physical environment they are in or the stakes change which makes the characters uncomfortable. Think about it: how often do you hate not being in control or not understanding what's ahead? Now transfer that emotion into a story. (Katniss leaving home for "The Hunger Games." She understood her world, but this new environment and challenge removes every sense of comfort she had.)
5. Focus on your ending. What do you want readers to feel at the end of your story? When that back cover is closed, what will they take with them? Well, throw the opposite emotion into the beginning and middle. "Lord of the Rings" is perfect for this. At almost every point the situation feels hopeless, but the characters hold on to hope right up to the end! It's why we love them as our heroes because we have so much to root for and have to know that when we, ourselves, hold on to hope, it's worth fighting for.

PROMPT 7: WRITE YOURSELF INTO A CORNER

A big trope in writing is writing the hardest conflict possible for the characters to overcome. Write a conflict for your characters that seems like there is no way out of.

Prompt 7

PROMPT 8: GET OUT OF THE CORNER

Now that you've intentionally written yourself into a corner, work through how your character will get out of the situation.

PROMPT 9: CONFLICT CONSEQUENCES

Every action has a reaction. Write a conflict and map out the ripple effect consequences that will result because of that action. How many are positive consequences? How many are negative? Is it worth the risk?

PROMPT 10: NO WAY OUT, NOW WHAT?

Not every conflict can be fixed. How do your characters move forward if they are unable to resolve a major or minor conflict in your story? Is there a way to work around it? What affect does it have on the characters emotionally? What does this failure contribute to the story?

Prompt 10

INTERNAL AND EXTERNAL: MATCHING THE INSIDES TO THE OUTSIDES

Melissa Koons

The strongest stories and characters are the ones that create both internal and external conflicts for the protagonist and other characters to overcome. The combination of conflicts creates a multi-dimensional plot and well-rounded characters who seem like actual people with actual struggles. While it's great to have both internal and external conflicts present, the real chemistry happens when the internal and external conflicts mirror each other and the resolution of one will trigger or aid in the resolution of the other. It can seem like a daunting task to try and create internal and external conflicts that are mirrors of each other, but once you know the technique it'll be easier than you might think.

Before you can start combining internal and external conflicts, you need to know the difference.

An internal conflict is a problem or challenge that the character is struggling to defeat internally on their own. This is the man vs self conflict. This can be an addiction, low self-confidence or self-esteem, a psychological disorder or trauma, a phobia or fear, a mental block or misperception, a lack of understanding, an over-inflated ego, a pattern of self-destructive behavior, a lack of skill, moral dilemmas, character flaws, etc.

Conversely, an external conflict is a problem or struggle that the character must overcome that is being placed on them by an external influence or something outside of themselves. The major external conflicts are: man vs man, man vs nature, man vs society, man vs machine, and man vs supernatural. This can be a super villain or another antagonist/character; natural disasters (not necessarily in the "trees are trying to kill you" way, looking at you M. Night.... but as in a plague, a volcano, an asteroid, global freezing, global warming, earthquake, hurricane, etc. disaster kind of way;) social expectations, pressures, or injustice; killer robots or technology such as a lab-created biochemical; and fate or a supernatural being like ghosts, gods, death, etc.

To craft an internal conflict for your character that reflects the external conflict you are going to need to do some pre-planning or outlining. If you hate outlining, you should get the Porcelain Prompts book devoted to helping you outline your novel, or just plan on doing some heavy revising after your first draft. Both are okay, but you are going to need to take care and pay attention. Crafting the internal and external conflicts requires you to plant seeds in your stories so that when the resolution comes it will make sense how a single resolution can wrap up both conflicts.

"The Truman Show" is a fantastic example of mirrored internal and external conflicts. If you haven't seen this fantastic film with Jim Carry and Ed Harris you need to. The story craft is brilliant. The premise is that Truman, played by Jim Carry in a dramatic role, is unknowingly part of an elaborate reality TV show that has followed him since his infancy. He was raised in a studio that was built to resemble the real world and producers and directors have controlled his entire life by adding plot points and "characters" to keep it interesting for viewers. The whole time Truman just thinks he's living life in a small town, unaware that every life event has been scripted for him from his father's death to who he would marry and that the whole world is actually watching him.

Truman's internal conflicts are carefully crafted both by the actual writers and by Ed Harris' character. Truman's "father" supposedly drowned which made Truman develop a fear of water. This was an external conflict created by Ed Harris to prevent Truman from trying to leave the small town/stage. However, it manifested into an internal conflict where Truman wants to explore, he wants to leave the town and see the world, but he has this intense fear that is stopping him. The external reflections of his fear that stop him from leaving are the actual studio executives and characters who put up physical barriers to prevent him from escaping.

Eventually, it all builds to *SPOILERS* an epic climax where Truman has discovered the truth and steals a boat to escape (facing his internal conflict and fear) while Ed Harris tries to stop him from leaving by creating a massive storm that should terrify him and force him to turn back (man vs man and man vs nature.) Truman pushes through and the resolution of both conflicts is that he defeats the external obstacles (the director of the show and the storm) as well as the internal (his fear of drowning/water) and is able to leave. This resolution allows his character growth because he finally gets to see the world—the real world—and make his own choices without his pressing fear and the studio which stopped him from doing so in the past. It's incredibly cathartic and a beautiful resolution fitting of the story.

Another example that might be a little more familiar is Disney's "Beauty and the Beast." The Beast is a prince who was cursed to appear monstrous because he was rude and self-centered. The internal conflict is that the prince is angry, selfish, and unkind. The external conflict is that he's trapped in the body of a monster and physically trapped within the castle itself, unable to leave lest he be cursed forever. It is through his relationship with Belle that he learns compassion, empathy, and selflessness. It is these changes to his internal conflict that allow her to fall in love with him and break the curse (the external conflict.) The resolution of the major conflict with the climax featuring Gaston and the mob attacking the castle is when Beast sacrifices himself, thus brining his internal conflict to an end and proving that he has changed and conquered those destructive behaviors of his past, and Belle's acceptance of him which breaks the curse and resolves the external conflict of his monstrous appearance and physical confinement.

Mirroring the internal and external conflicts gives the final conflict and climax of the story extra oomph and creates a resolution that is cathartic and resonates with the audience because it wraps up everything all at once. It takes practice but once you start thinking about internal and external conflicts while you're developing your characters and story then it will all start coming together.

PROMPT 11: IT'S ALL GOING DOWN

Characters experience both internal and external conflicts. The best conflicts are the ones that mirror each other. Create an internal conflict and an external conflict that mirror the same underlying struggle.

51

Prompt 11

PROMPT 12: RUN AWAY

Give your protagonist a paralyzing fear. Create a conflict that includes that fear. How can your protagonist resolve the conflict without overcoming or facing their fear? Can they figure out a way to work around it?

Prompt 12

PROMPT 13: FACING DEMONS

For a cathartic resolution, the protagonist will often have to face a fear that they have in order to resolve the conflict. Choose two conflicts (i.e.: Man vs. Man, Man vs. Nature) and create a fear for each conflict that your protagonist will have to overcome in order to resolve it.

PROMPT 14: CLAUSTROPHOBIA

One of the best ways to increase conflict is to confine characters. When you're trapped (physically or emotionally) it causes more stress and illogical decisions made out of panic. Write about people who are trapped in some way, shape, or form.

65

MAGIC FIX: THE LAZY WAY TO RESOLVE CONFLICT

Melissa Koons

We've all been there as readers or viewers when a story has set up an incredible conflict—an against-all-odds scenario—where tensions are high and the stakes are dire, yet the resolution falls short and feels not only anticlimactic, but like a cheap cop-out. Instead of rising to the occasion, the writers used a magic fix-all that resolved the conflict suddenly, quickly, and often without much resistance. When we are reading or viewing these resolutions, it feels like the writer didn't know where to go or how to get their characters out of the mess they found themselves in, and that really puts a damper on the entire story arc that built to that point. While it is annoying to have everything wrapped up without any effort, it is also a little insulting to have the characters' entire journey trivialized and reduced to a magic fix-all solution.

Some of the most popular and well-known stories are guilty of this. One such book (and film) that falls prey to the magic-fix resolution is "War of the Worlds." "War of the Worlds" is a corner stone of science fiction, both the book and the multiple film adaptations. The reason it is a classic is because it creates a world and scenario that are equally terrifying and entertaining—until the resolution. Martians (or random aliens depending on the interpretation) invade Earth and have really got the human race on the ropes. It's not looking good for our species; the Martians have bigger machines, more advanced technology, and impenetrable defense shields that render our weapons useless. Everything is building toward what appears to be the end of humanity and the world as we know it until, quite suddenly and without any foreshadowing, the shields power down and the aliens start dying. Turns out, there are no germs or bacteria on Mars and therefore they have no immunity to the tiny organisms and end up perishing. The battle is over, the world is won, and the victor is the human race by default.

Scientifically, this ending makes complete sense and is a brilliant twist. However, what makes this resolution fall into the magic fix category is that it literally contributed nothing to the main characters' arcs. The story focuses on the humans and their attempts to escape and/or overpower the Martian invaders, yet the resolution has nothing to do with them. The humans didn't figure it out, they didn't plot some biological warfare, and they weren't even the ones to carry the disease that got the aliens sick. Nothing. It was total luck of the draw and came out of nowhere to save the day. That's the other reason this resolution is a magic fix: there was no foreshadowing at all. There's nothing in the earlier narrative to suggest deadly bacteria as a possibility. There are no hints of illness—a flu epidemic or something—to allude that maybe these little organisms that hurt us, could also hurt other beings on an even larger scale since they have had zero exposure. They're just suddenly there, killing aliens! It's a lazy solution that could have actually been awesome if it was worked into the narrative properly. (Just give the little girl a cold, Spielberg! For goodness sake…)

Another big offender of the magic fix resolution is "The Matrix Trilogy." The first film was phenomenal, there is no argument about that. The second film fell into stride, and seemed to be building toward an extreme existential crises and a (rather on the nose) metaphor for the relationship with a divine creator/architect and their creation. What is our purpose in this world?! I'll never know because the Matrix never finished telling me… Instead, the third film took a hard left and ventured into uncharted territory. Why is Agent Smith going crazy and taking over the Matrix? No seriously, why? What is his motivation? He'll die, too, if he destroys it. I can get on board with the whole "Agent Smith is a computer virus" idea—it's cute in a computer pun kind of way, but following this narrative made the first two films mean absolutely nothing. The architect God guy? Pffft, who needs him? We'll just leave that plot hole and move on, never to mention it or that weird white room again. No answers for you there! The hundreds of years war between robots and humans that was the whole reason Neo was pulled from the Matrix in the first place and the super huge plot point in the first two movies that gave Neo's character arc its significance and meaning (and, oh yeah, Trinity and Orpheus' arcs, too)? Ha! We'll wrap that up with one conversation and a "good faith" agreement that the robots will leave humans alone and return their free will as long as Neo plays Anti-Virus scanner and destroys Agent Smith. New energy source for the robots to survive and use to power themselves and their civilization? I'm sure they'll figure it out and not go back to harvesting human babies. They promised, after all.

"Chosen One" be darned, the resolution reduces the hero of the entire human race to fighting off a swarm of Hugo Weavings. Neo's character development, his coming into his chosen one power, his team building and training with Orpheus, his romance with Trinity—nope! It all means nothing as it had no impact whatsoever to actually reaching a truce with the machines and freeing every one of the Matrix. Like, seriously. Neo could have gone through none of it and still achieved the same outcome. He was a programmer and hacker! With the Agent Smith virus, he could have just hacked into the Matrix from the outside and done a system wipe while updating their firewalls. No one needs to know jujitsu or how to fly to do that. He literally had all the skills when they pulled him from the Matrix. With this final resolution that took three movies to build to, the story actually could have been wrapped up in about 30 minutes with significantly less character deaths and a nice steak dinner for everyone (curse you Cypher!)

These are just two of many examples where the writers didn't stick the landing. The resolution isn't just a solve to the major conflict, it's what the whole story and characters have been building toward. Give everyone a solid send off by making your resolution worthy of the struggles, hardships, and conflicts that the characters and readers have endured. Don't pull a solution out of thin air that negates the entire progress and development up to that point, and don't hand it to the characters like a treat: "Oh you made it this far? Good job, I'll stop doing evil things, now." Don't be lazy; do more than a magic fix and make your story mean something with the resolution.

PROMPT 15: RESOLVE WITHOUT MAGIC FIX

Create a conflict that can only be resolved by a magical fix solution. Now, remove the elements that led to the magical fix. How can your characters resolve the conflict without it?

Prompt 15

PROMPT 16: MCGUFFIN

A common trope in creating conflict is a McGuffin, the object a character has to acquire in order to solve a problem (The Ark in Raiders of the Lost Ark, Loki's Spear in The Avengers, etc.) Create a McGuffin and a conflict around it.

Prompt 16

Prompt 16

PROMPT 17: COMMON GROUND

Sometimes two characters who oppose each other join together as allies against a greater conflict by finding a commonality between them. Write a story about two characters who seem like total opposites of one another, but find resolution through a single commonality.

Prompt 17

Prompt 17

LET'S TALK ABOUT MARTHA

Melissa Koons

Writing conflict is hard, but writing a good resolution is harder. Conflict can build for a multitude of reasons, and often it has ripple effects and consequences that cause more problems both short and long term. A good resolution needs to address all these aspects of the conflict and manage to conclude them. The resolution needs to resonate and feel natural for the characters and story. It can feel disappointing, unsatisfactory, or even disingenuous to a reader or viewer when only part of the conflict is resolved but the rest is left open-ended or forgotten altogether. Worse yet, is when the conflict is hastily wrapped up to move on without consideration as to whether or not the resolution is true to the characters or the situation. This type of cheap resolution is glaringly obvious and not only is it an insult to the reader who stuck with the story just for this moment, but it also undermines the conflict itself.

Any impact or message the conflict had is suddenly devalued with an awful resolution. The stakes that had been raised now look ridiculous, as do the characters and their struggles. Not only has it just made the characters' arcs pointless, it has made the time the reader or viewer has invested worthless as well.

At this point, it should not be news that "Batman vs. Superman" (released by Warner Brothers in 2016) was a huge disappointment to viewers and fans. Disregarding the special effects, too many plot lines, too many plot holes, and too many good ideas abandoned for… who knows what—the biggest let down of the film was the resolution to Batman and Superman's beef: Martha.

"Batman vs. Superman" made one of the worst storytelling mistakes that destroyed the quality of the film and turned the entire plot into a joke. That mistake? Coming up with a cheap resolution just to move things along and thus undermining the conflict. Batman was fighting against Superman because he, and most of the world, feared that Superman was a danger to Earth and his mere presence on the planet would turn Earth into a giant target for crazy alien shenanigans (they're not wrong…) Good ol' Bruce Wayne also has a bone to pick because in the film "Man of Steel," Superman got a little too wrapped up in defeating the big alien invasion that he kind destroyed a city and, consequently, many people died as collateral damage.

Batman's motivations for wanting to take Superman out are understandable. Viewers understand his plight, and many would agree with him after watching a dust-covered Ben Affleck hold a dirty, crying child. The viewer is on board with his conflict.

Likewise, the viewer sees Superman's guilt and knows that he just wants to help. The viewer sees Clark Kent's personal struggle to do what is right, and yet he can't seem to catch a break. The viewer wants him to succeed. The viewer wants to see Superman take to the sky and save the day, and they are on board with his conflict, too.

The conflict between Batman and Superman was set-up well. Both had motivations to be in the positions they were in. Both were equally right, and equally wrong. Both should win, and both should lose. It was the perfect moral tug-of-war.

Then it was all ruined. Their motivations, their drive, their individual struggles—in the end they all meant nothing. Why? Because of Martha.

Instead of carrying out the battle and letting it reach a natural and cathartic resolution, the resolution is rushed just so that the film can introduce Doomsday and get to the "cool" fight sequence. In the film the two came to blows in a deserted part of the city (we know how Bruce feels about collateral damage.) It's invincible alien man vs. squishy middle-aged guy in a metal bat suit. Tensions are high. Mean things are said. Superman wants to talk, Batman has a tantrum. It's all as you'd expect. It looks like Batman doesn't stand a chance but the stakes are raised when Bruce finds a way to level the playing field. With the help of some kryptonite gas bombs, Batman turns the tables. Batman has the upper hand and it's all over for dear, Clark Kent. Superman is weakened and knows the deathblow is coming; in his gasping final moments, he delivers the pathetic line that ends up being the trigger for the resolution: "Tell Martha I'm sorry."

That one line is the catalyst for the resolution that cheapens the entire conflict and makes the first two-thirds of the movie pointless. So how does Martha ruin everything? Turns out Martha is Superman's mom. Not just that, but—surprise! —Batman's murdered mother's name was also Martha. Hearing the name of his dead mom suddenly triggers the lost compassion in Bruce and he decides to forget all about his earlier motivations: getting vengeance for the thousands of innocents Superman inadvertently killed, protecting the world from a reckless alien, saving Gotham. Screw it. Superman's mother shares the name as Batman's dead mom and that makes them best buds now. Forget everything else!

Now, this could have worked. It is totally believable that, as he is faced with defeat, Clark's guilt and love for his mother would be his final words. Still, this line feels flat and there's a reason for that. It's forced. What guy calls his mother by her first name when he's about to be killed? No one. That's who. Its only purpose is to trigger Batman so that Bruce gets all melancholy and throws down his weapon; "My mother's name was Martha, too."

Seriously. If you feel upset just reading this, then you are feeling the right feelings. That was an awful resolution to a logically built-up conflict. If Batman and Superman were five-year-olds on the playground, I might understand that kind of resolution. However, that was not the case. What is most upsetting about this resolution is that it completely drops all the very legitimate conflicts Batman and Superman had with each other. The conflict that was pushing their character arcs and development was wrapped up with a single name: Martha. Not only does that name dissolve their conflict, but it also crumbles the entire story. Batman lets go of his anger for dirty, orphaned child, and Superman no longer feels the need to defend himself and his usefulness on Earth. Neither character evolves, nor neither character answers for their crimes. That name eliminates all consequences of their earlier actions.

A good resolution needs to have consequences for the conflict. The consequences should help your characters grow or learn something important. Resolution is all about wrapping up the arcs that led the story and characters to the climax, but it also needs to give meaning to what the characters, readers, and viewers endured. Martha was not growth. Martha was not a lesson. Martha was not meaningful. Don't pull a Martha.

PROMPT 18: LEARNING CURVE

At the start, your protagonist should not possess all the abilities they will need to overcome the major conflict they face. Write a story where your protagonist learns the skills they will need in order to succeed and resolve the conflict. What are the obstacles they face that teach them these skills? How many tries does it take them before they master it?

Prompt 18

PROMPT 19: SPEED BUMPS

There should be one major conflict your protagonist is working toward, but along they way there should encounter several smaller conflicts that work to prepare them for facing the major one later. Outline a major conflict and five smaller ones that your protagonist encounters on their journey.

Prompt 19

PROMPT 20: UNEXPECTED CONFLICT

Your neighbor uses your wireless printer by accident. What is on the sheet and what do you do about it? Does it create a conflict with your neighbor or a conflict because you become involved with whatever is on the paper?

MEET THE CREATORS

Thomas A. Fowler

At the age of 11, Thomas A. Fowler saw Jurassic Park. It was all nerdy as hell from there. Especially when he stuck around for the end credits and saw "Based on the novel by Michael Crichton." He went straight from the movie theater, walked down the mall to a Walden Books.

Since then, he's written movies, plays, short-stories and books. While he sticks primarily to science-fiction, he dabbles elsewhere. He holds an MBA in Marketing from Regis University and was a former Content Creator at a full-service ad agency in Denver, Colorado. Now, he devotes that skill set to a freelance career and to helping authors live their dream of getting published.

Somewhere, between writing and advertising, he tries to be a loving husband and responsible father.

Marketing Director at Spine Press & Post Publishing Services

Melissa Koons

Melissa Koons has always had a passion for books and creative writing. It may have started with Berenstain Bears by Stan and Jan Berenstain, but it didn't take long for authors like Lucy Culliford Babbit, Tolkien, and Robert Jordan to follow. From a young age she knew she wanted to share her love for stories with the world.

She has written and published one novel, multiple short stories, and poetry. She has a BA in English and Secondary Education from the University of Northern Colorado.

A former middle and high school English teacher, she now devotes her career to publishing, editing, writing, and tutoring hoping to inspire and help writers everywhere achieve their goals. When she's not working, she's taking care of her two turtles and catching up on the latest comic book franchise.

Publications Director at Spine Press and Post Publishing Services

HOPE YOU REACHED PROFOUND RESOLUTIONS, BOTH IN YOUR WRITING & ON THE THRONE!

BUT DID YOU KNOW THERE ARE 5 OTHER VOLUMES AND WE'RE DROPPING MORE SOON?

FIND THEM ALL AT

PORCELAINPROMPTS.COM

10590569R00060

Printed in Great Britain
by Amazon